SPE
CARTOON
1999

Edited by
Michael Heath

P

PROFILE BOOKS

in association with

The Spectator

First published
in book form in Great Britain in 1999
by Profile Books Ltd
58A Hatton Garden, London EC1N 8LX
in association with
The Spectator
56 Doughty Street, London WC1N 2LL

© The Spectator, 1999

Printed and bound in Great Britain by
St Edmundsbury Press Ltd

A CIP catalogue record for this book is available from
the British Library.

ISBN 1 86197 150 8

Lost your sense of humour watching comedy shows on television? Learn to laugh again by viewing this collection of cartoons from *The Spectator*. No batteries required.

Michael Heath

Government Health Warning
Some of the cartoons can cause convulsions

"And cut down on the royal waving!"

"It's not like I expected."

"Aren't you rather young to be on first-name terms?"

"Two's company, three's a cult."

Marriage on the rocks

"Do I take it that's a 'No'?"

*"Ooh, wait till the neighbours see this,
you getting your name in the paper!"*

*"Say, what kind of mood were you in when you made this?
I get bad vibes eating it."*

*"John, wake up!… Look at the state of you —
covered in slugs!"*

"Oh, come dear. You had a good run. You've stayed overrated for far longer than I thought you would."

"And then the poltergeist tidied Adrian's bedroom."

"Was that the Earth moving or an Indian bomb test?"

"Now that you're redundant isn't it time you dispensed with that stuffy get-up?"

"Er, actually I brought the baby with me."

"No thanks — I'm trying to give them up."

"Emergency exits are located on each side of the aircraft…"

"Is this all we do? Sneak out here and chew nicotine gum?"

"Good God, son — you're too large for polka dots!"

"So what's all this about using eye of newt, toe of frog, wool of bat, tongue of dog, adder's fork, blind-worm's sting, lizard's leg and howlet's wing, you old hag!"

HIS MASTER'S VOICE MAIL

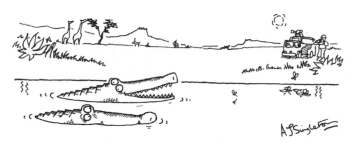

"I like to think of myself as a tourist trap."

"Darren's a typical teenager — all he ever does is grunt."

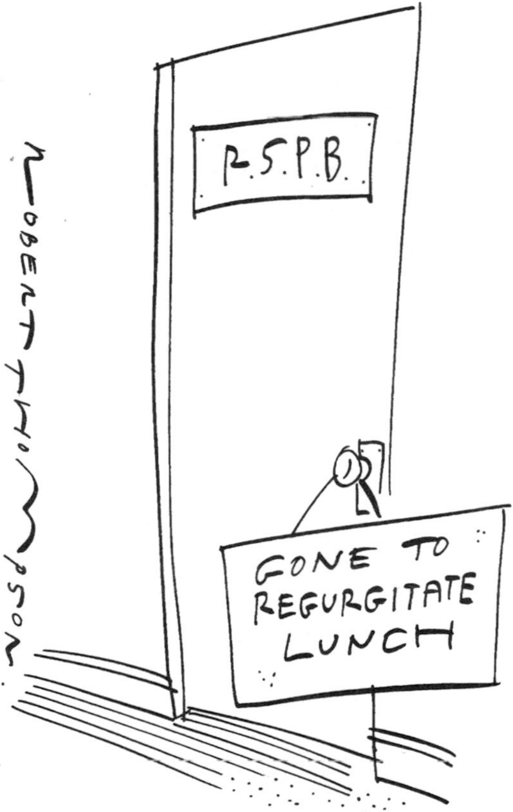
R.S.P.B.
GONE TO REGURGITATE LUNCH

"Sounds to me like you've had a stroke."

"How interesting. I've never met a
vegetarian vulture before."

"Uh-oh!"

It was going to be a long day at the Post Office

"I'll watch it in my room, on the portable".

"Don't inquire of his family. His wife's been done for shoplifting, his two kids are doing corrective training, and his dog has bitten a policeman."

"He should be approached with caution as he is known to smoke."

"I can't read... that's a handicap, right?"

"It's all very well, but that wheelchair cost me a fortune."

*"Very well, 8.95 million.
Now, how about a senior citizen discount?"*

"Do you have any that looks like paint?"

"Please take a seat."

"You're not going to throw that shoebox away are you?"

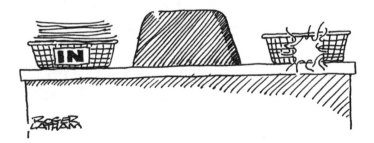

"It's not exactly the career in finance I had in mind…"

NICK DOWNES

"We have plonk, sir, but not cheap plonk."

*"Waitress, could you come over here
and pour me some more scorn, please?"*

"Gentlemen, this is a power restaurant. If you must discuss your families, please keep your voices down."

"Eureka! I've lost it!"

'SPARE SOME CHANGE' BY HENRY MOORE

SALVADOR DALI EXHIBITION

"He got the mouth right."

"I suppose you could call me old-fashioned."

ROBERT THOMPSON

"Next on The Time Channel—two o'clock."

SIPRESS

"They must be out enjoying the countryside.
Their chainsaw isn't here."

"Jean… if you could fill in this questionnaire on how you've enjoyed the evening."

"These people aren't trendy. Don't get four-letter wording it."

"Hey, Eddie — check this out."

"Until you win the lottery, you don't know what it's like to be part of a persecuted minority."

"The other man's crass is always crasser."

"Tell me, which tattooist are you using these days?"

An ineluctable law of rail travel

"I liked you better before I liked you."

"Hi! I'm on the train!"

"Damn! I really thought we were on to something with this yo-yo idea."